CW00402411

MADAM SAMURAI

Based on an original idea by Gael McLaughlin

Drawn by David Hitchcock
Written by Gary Young

www.madamsamurai.com

Editor: Shane Chebsey
Published by Scar Comics
Copyright © Madam Samurai Properties Limited 2010. All rights reserved.

For Scar Comics
Art Director: Andrew Richmond
Assisted by Sam Morgan

Madam Samurai Volume One. Published by Scar Comics, 2010. First Printing.
All contents of this book are copyright Madam Samurai Properties Ltd.
No portion of this book may be reproduced in any form without prior permission of the
copyright owner except for review purposes.
All events and characters portrayed are entirely fictional unless otherwise stated.
Any resemblance of persons living or dead is entirely coincidental.

ISBN: 978-0-9553697-3-5

To find out more about Scar Comics visit the official website at: www.scarcomics.com

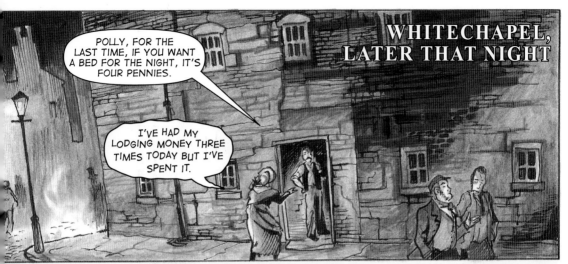

9th CENTURY JAPAN, THIRTY YEARS EARLIER

I MUST HONOUR YOUR FATHER AND FOLLOW HIM IN DEATH.

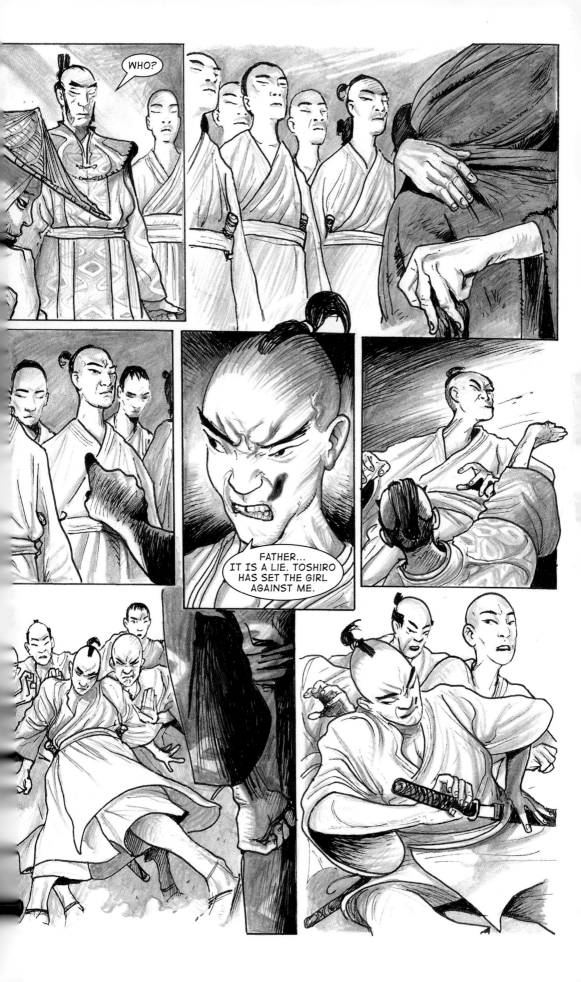

THE CHILD HAS NEVER UTTERED A SOUND – EVEN WHEN SHE CAME OUT OF HER MOTHER'S WOMB.

MY DAUGHTER DIED AS MY GRANDDAUGHTER LIVED.

AND THE FATHER? WELL, MY DAUGHTER...

...SHE WAS ...ATTACKED AND... AFTERWARDS SHE FOUND OUT SHE WAS PREGNANT.

THE MAN WHO ATTACKED HER...VANISHED.

DO YOU KNOW HOW DANGEROUS IT IS FOR HIM TO BE HERE?

IF THEY FIND OUT HE IS STILL ALIVE, MEN WILL COME AND KILL US ALL.

YOU CAN'T FOOL ME. I KNOW WHAT YOU WANT.

YOU WANT HIM TO TEACH YOU TO BE A WARRIOR. TO BE A SAMURAI AND FIND HE WHO DISHONOURED YOUR MOTHER.

HE IS NOT A SAMURAI ANY MORE. HE IS A RONIN. NO BETTER THAN A BANDIT.

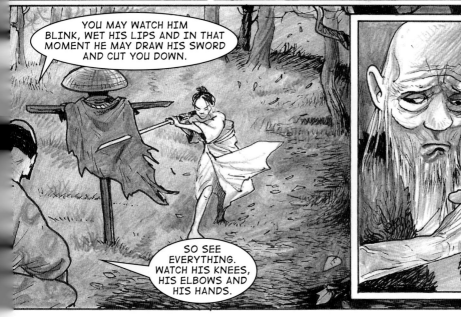

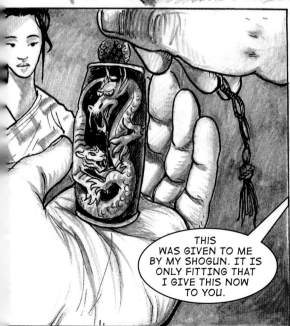

PLEASE MASTER! DON'T HURT HER. SHE DOESN'T KNOW WHAT SHE IS DOING.

I BEG YOU, SPARE HER!

DEAD MEN CAN'T TEACH PEASANT GIRLS HOW TO FIGHT LIKE A SAMURAI. I'LL SPARE HER LIFE IF YOU TAKE ME TO THE MAN THIS SWORD BELONGS TO.

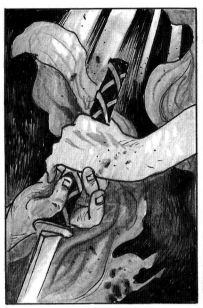

HEY!

WHENEVER YOU WANT TO STICK THAT SWORD IN ME, I'LL GIVE YOU THE TIME.

WHAT DO WE DO ABOUT THE OLD MAN?

KILL HIM.

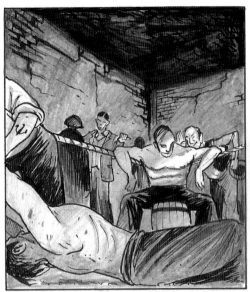

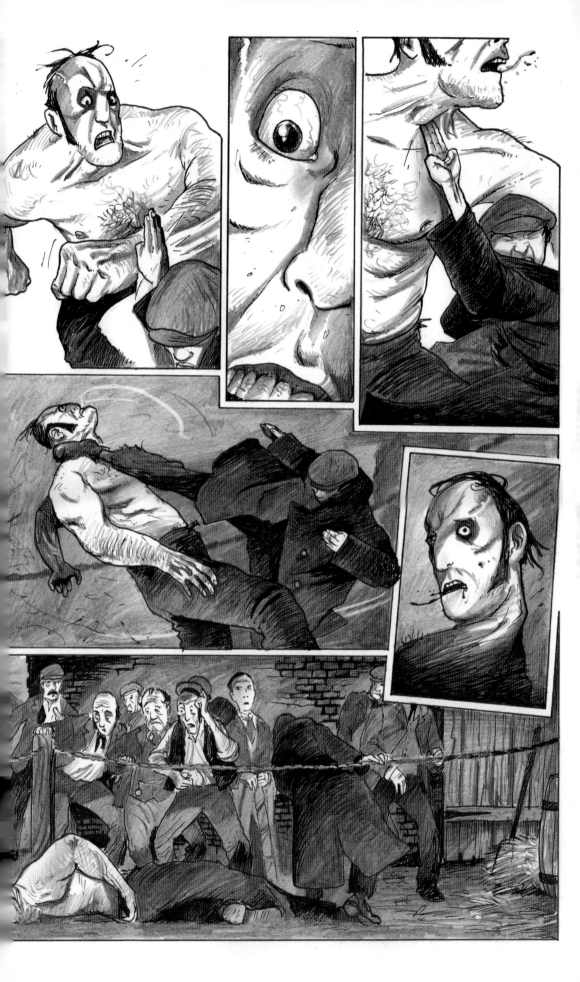

I DIDN'T REALISE YOU WERE A... I THOUGHT YOU WERE A BOY.

YOU ARE PRETTY. I BET YOU SCRUB UP REAL NICE.

IF YOU WANT TO MAKE SOME REAL MONEY, I HAVE A FRIEND. HE'LL PUT YOU TO WORK.

YOU WON'T HAVE TO FIGHT BIG MEN LIKE THAT. YOU'LL WEAR PRETTY DRESSES AND MEET NICE GENTLEMEN.

EVERYONE AGAINST THE WALL!

PUT THAT THING AWAY. COME ON! STAND UP STRAIGHT!

DON'T YOU CLEVER WIT... YOU C... LITTLE T... GET... THERE... THE OTH...

HELLO, INSPECTOR REID... THE LAST TIME I SAW THAT RED FACE YOU HAD YOUR PANTS ROUND YOUR ANKLES.

OI, REID! WHAT IS ALL THIS?

IT'S INSPECTOR REID TO YOU, YOU FERRET-FACED NONCE!

SERGEANT LEACH, SEARCH THIS MAN!

WHAT'S THIS?

WHAT DOES IT LOOK LIKE? IT'S A KNIFE.

YEAH AND WHAT DO YOU DO WITH IT?

IT'S FOR MY JOB.

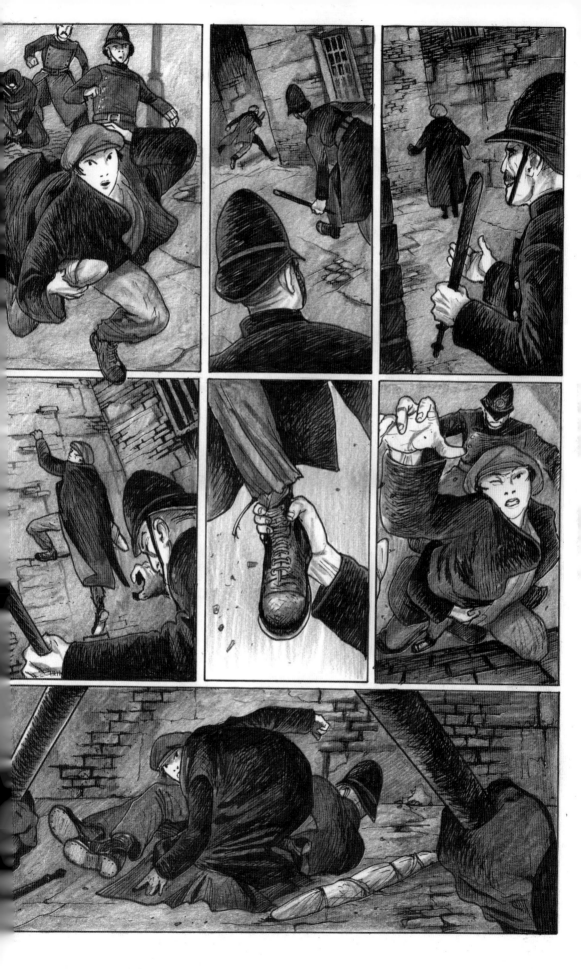

END OF BOOK ONE

DAVID HITCHCOCK

David Hitchcock has been drawing comics for as long as he can remember, but only deemed them suitable for public consumption in the mid 90s.

In 1999 he self published his first graphic novel masterpiece *Spirit of the Highwayman* meeting critical acclaim from the world of comics.

David's instantly noticeable style returned for such favourites as his spin on Jack the Ripper with the superb *Whitechapel Freak*, and then again picking up a coveted Eagle Award in 2005 for *Springheeled Jack*.

In 2008 he published a collection of his best short comic strips called *'Gothic'* much to the delight of fans at the British International Comics Show as queues for his sketches rivalled those of comics legend Michael Golden.

Also look out for David's work in the Accent UK anthologies illustrating the stories of Leah Moore and John Reppion.

GARY YOUNG

Gary is a UK based screenwriter who has five feature films to his credit, including *Harry Brown* starring Sir Michael Caine. Gary has been a great fan and collector of comic books since childhood, but *Madam Samurai* is his first venture into writing one. It's been such a rewarding experience that he's now developing more comic book project alongside his slate of feature projects.

GAEL McLAUGHLIN

Gael is an up-and-coming UK based film produce with a slate of genre films in development including *Madam Samurai*. She came up with the initial concept for the story and commissioned Gary Young to write it. When he then suggested that the script was also perfect graphic novel material Gael sought out a publisher and discovered the ideal partner in Scar Comics- and the rest is history! She is a big fan of fantasy and adventure stories and now has plans to develop more of her script concepts into graphic novels, games and other media.